A DOZEN A
TRUMPET SONGBOOK
Christmas

THE WILLIS MUSIC COMPANY

Unto Us A Boy Is Born

Words by George Ratcliffe Woodward
Music Traditional
Arranged by Christopher Hussey

TRACKS 1–2

෧∾ *Watch out for...*

- The time signature **4/4** — this tells you there are four quarter note beats in each measure.

- The dynamic marks, which tell you how loudly or softly to play.
  p = *piano*, tells you to play 'softly'.   ***f*** = *forte*, tells you to play 'loudly'.

- Your articulation — try to play smoothly in a *legato* style.

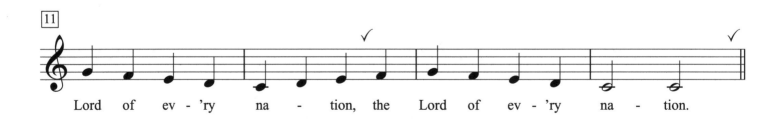

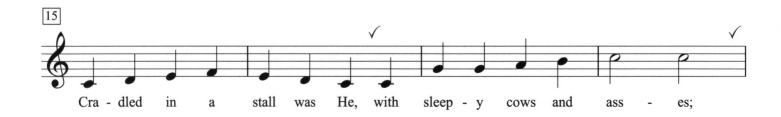

but the ve - ry beasts could see that He all men sur - pass - es, that

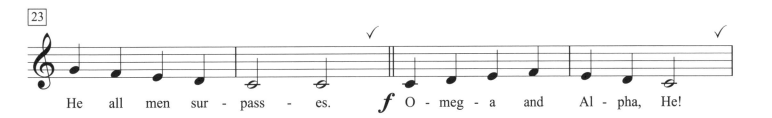

He all men sur - pass - es. 𝆑 O - meg - a and Al - pha, He!

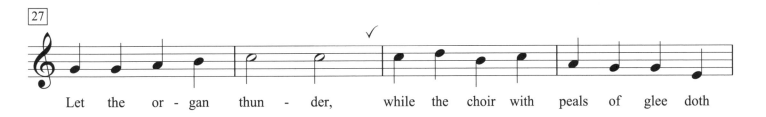

Let the or - gan thun - der, while the choir with peals of glee doth

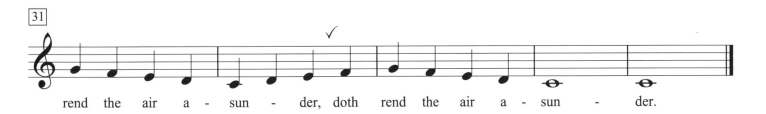

rend the air a - sun - der, doth rend the air a - sun - der.

Away In A Manger

 TRACKS
3–4

Words Traditional
Music by William Kirkpatrick
Arranged by Christopher Hussey

Watch out for...

- The time signature **3/4** — this tells you there are three quarter note beats in each measure.

- The dotted half notes — which last three beats, and the eighth notes — which last for half a beat and can be joined as a pair like this:

- The *fermata* on the last note — this tells you to hold the note for longer than its written duration.

Sweetly

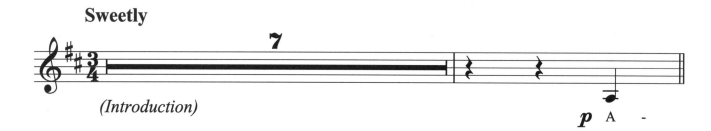

(Introduction)

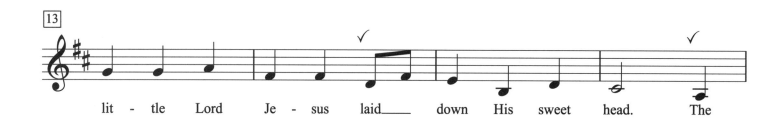

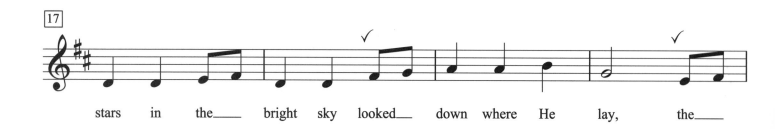

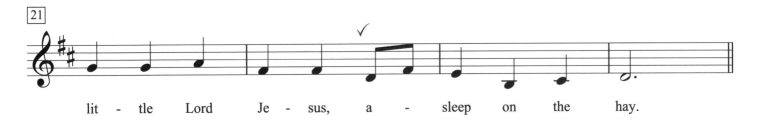

lit - tle Lord Je - sus, a - sleep on the hay.

f Be near me, Lord___ Je - sus, I___

ask Thee to stay close___ by me for ev - er, and___

love me, I pray. Bless all the dear___ chil - dren in___

Thy ten - der care, and___ take us to heav - en to___

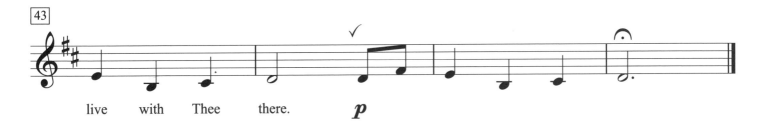

live with Thee there. *p*

O Come, All Ye Faithful

Words & Music by John Francis Wade
Arranged by Christopher Hussey

TRACKS
5–6

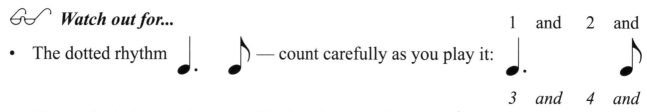

Watch out for...

- The dotted rhythm ♩. ♪ — count carefully as you play it:
- Your articulation — play smoothly, in a *legato* style.

Majestically

O come, all ye faith - ful, joy - ful and tri -

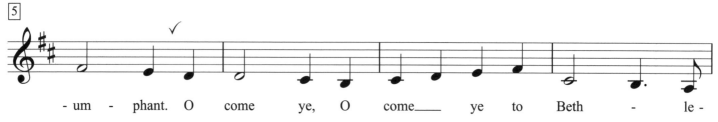

- um - phant. O come ye, O come___ ye to Beth - le -

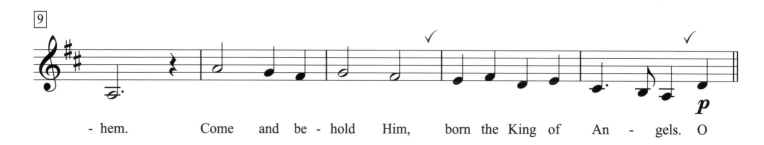

- hem. Come and be - hold Him, born the King of An - gels. O

come, let us a - dore Him, O come, let us a - dore Him, O

7

come let us a - dore Him, Christ, the Lord.

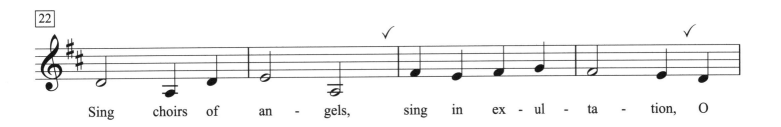

Sing choirs of an - gels, sing in ex - ul - ta - tion, O

sing all you cit - i - zens of heav'n a - bove.

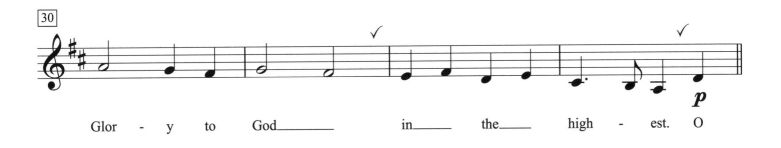

Glor - y to God in the high - est. O

come, let us a - dore Him, O come, let us a - dore Him, O

come let us a - dore Him, Christ, the Lord.

See, Amid The Winter's Snow

Words by Edward Caswall
Music by John Goss
Arranged by Christopher Hussey

 TRACKS 7–8

⌒ *Watch out for...*

- The two-note slurs in this song ♩ ♩ — join these notes together as smoothly as possible.

- The octave leaps in measures 18–19 and 34–35.

Expressively

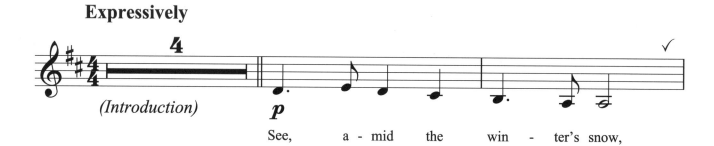

(Introduction) **p**

See, a - mid the win - ter's snow,

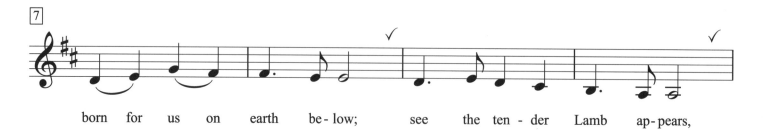

born for us on earth be - low; see the ten - der Lamb ap - pears,

f

prom - ised from e - ter - nal years. Hail, thou ev - er - bless - ed morn!

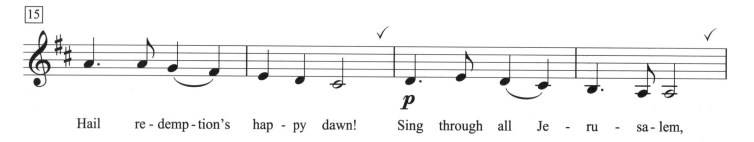

p

Hail re - demp - tion's hap - py dawn! Sing through all Je - ru - sa - lem,

Christ is born in Beth - le - hem! Lo, with - in a man - ger lies

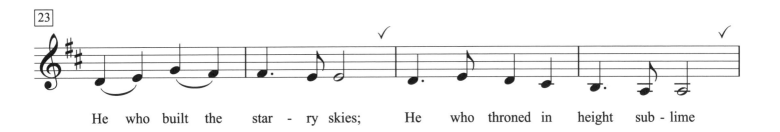

He who built the star - ry skies; He who throned in height sub - lime

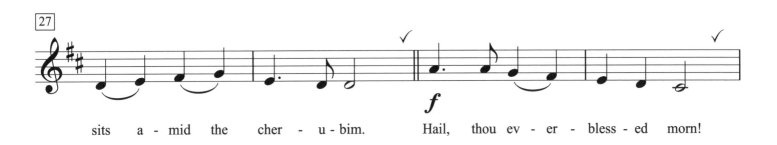

sits a - mid the cher - u - bim. *f* Hail, thou ev - er - bless - ed morn!

Hail re - demp - tion's hap - py dawn! Sing through all Je - ru - sa - lem,

Christ is born in Beth - le - hem! *p*

Silent Night

Words by Joseph Mohr
Music by Franz Gruber
Arranged by Christopher Hussey

TRACKS
9–10

Watch out for...

- The dotted rhythm ♩. ♪ — count carefully as you play it:
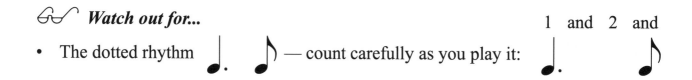

- The breath marks — they are less frequent now, only once every four measures. You can add more in, if you find the phrases too long for one breath.

Peacefully

(Introduction) *p* Si - lent night, ho - ly

night.   All   is   calm,   all   is   bright,

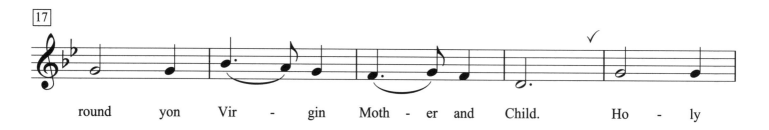

round   yon   Vir - gin   Moth - er   and   Child.   Ho - ly

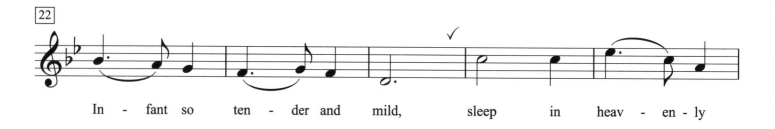

In - fant so   ten - der and   mild,   sleep   in   heav - en - ly

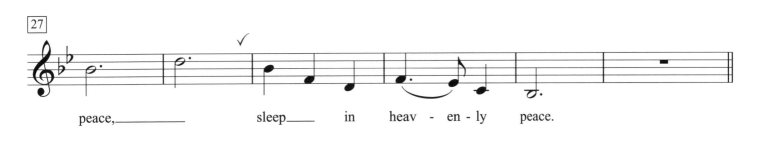

peace,_____ sleep___ in heav - en - ly peace.

f Si - lent night, ho - ly night.

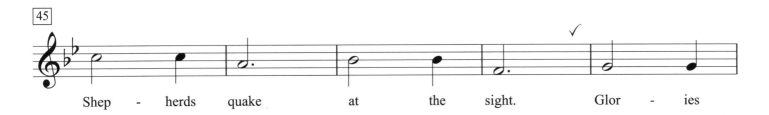

Shep - herds quake at the sight. Glor - ies

stream___ from heav - en a - far, heav'n - ly hosts___ sing

"Al - le - lu - ia: Christ, the Sav - iour is

born,_____ Christ,___ the Sav - iour is born!"

p

Angels From The Realms Of Glory

**TRACKS
11–12**

Words by James Montgomery
Music Traditional English
Arranged by Christopher Hussey

ᬡ *Watch out for...*

- The new dymanic marks — **mp** = *mezzo piano*, telling you to play 'moderately softly', and **mf** = *mezzo forte*, telling you to play 'moderately loudly'.

  Follow each change and you'll find the dynamic variety will help make your playing more expressive.

Smoothly

An - gels from the____ realms of glor - y, wing your flight o'er____

all the earth. Ye, who sang cre - a - tion's stor - y,

13

now pro - claim Mess - i - ah's birth. Come_____

mf

_____ and_____ wor - ship

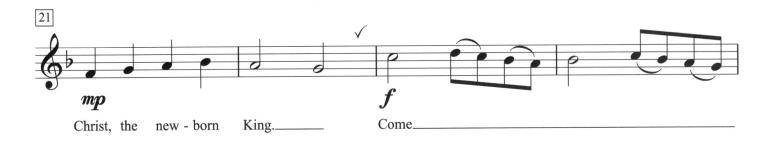

mp

Christ, the new - born King._____ Come_____

f

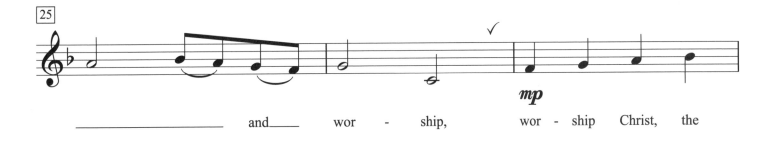

_____ and_____ wor - ship,   wor - ship Christ, the

mp

new - born King.

4

mf   p

Ding Dong! Merrily On High

Words by George Ratcliffe Woodward
Music Traditional
Arranged by Christopher Hussey

TRACKS 13–14

ᎧᎧ *Watch out for...*

- The four-note slurs in this song 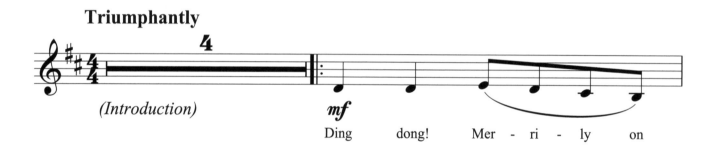 — join this group of eighth notes together as smoothly as possible.

- The very long six-bar phrase in measures 13–18 and 29–34 — if you're finding them tricky to play in one breath, add some more breaths while you build up to it.

- The *repeat* signs ‖: :‖ — when you reach the 'end repeat' in measure 20, repeat back from the 'start repeat' in measure 5, and play on.

Triumphantly

(Introduction)   *mf*

Ding   dong!   Mer - ri - ly   on

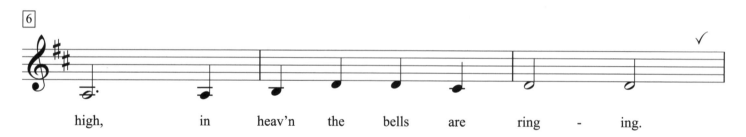

high,   in   heav'n   the   bells   are   ring - ing.

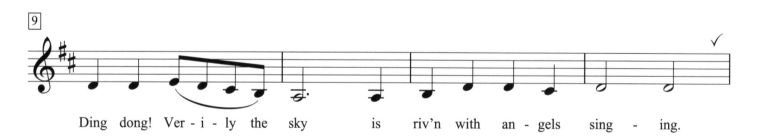

Ding   dong!   Ver - i - ly   the   sky   is   riv'n   with   an - gels   sing - ing.

Glor -

- - - - - - - - -i - a,   Ho -

-san - na   in   ex - cel - sis!   Pray   you,   du - ti - ful - ly

prime   your   mat - in   chime, ye   ring - ers.   May   you   beau - ti - ful - ly

rhyme   your   eve - time   song,   ye   sing - ers.   Glor - -

- - - - - - - -

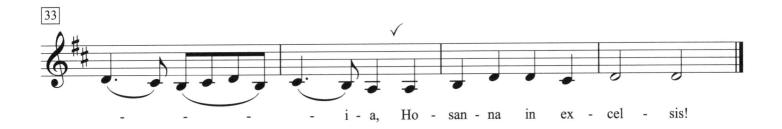

- - - - -i - a,   Ho - san - na   in   ex - cel - sis!

Once In Royal David's City

Words by Cecil Frances Humphreys Alexander
Music by Henry John Gauntlett
Arranged by Christopher Hussey

TRACKS
15–16

 Watch out for...

- The four-note slurs — join these notes together as smoothly as possible.

- The *tie* in measures 3 and 19 — when two notes of the same pitch are joined with a *tie*, you don't play the second note again, but hold the first note for the duration of both notes.

Broadly

mp

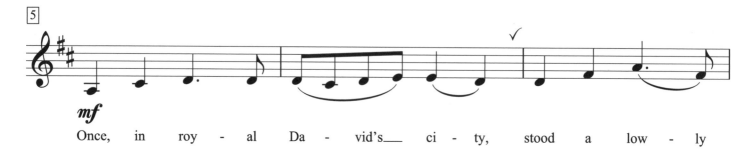

mf

Once, in roy - al Da - vid's_ ci - ty, stood a low - ly

cat - tle_ shed, where a moth - er laid_ her_ Ba - by,

in a man - ger for_ His_ bed.   Ma - ry was that

f

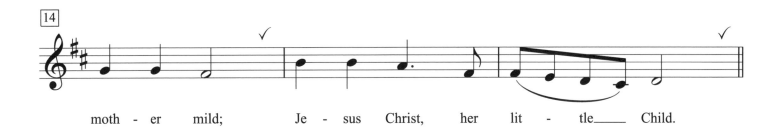

moth - er mild; Je - sus Christ, her lit - tle___ Child.

mf

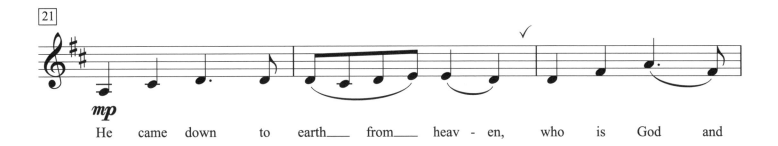

mp

He came down to earth___ from___ heav - en, who is God and

Lord___ of___ all. And His shel - ter was___ a___ sta - ble,

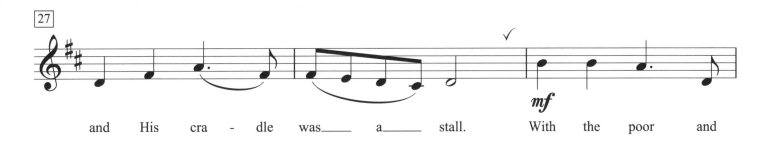

mf

and His cra - dle was___ a___ stall. With the poor and

mean and low - ly, lived on earth our Sa - viour___ ho - ly.

The Holly And The Ivy

Traditional English
Arranged by Christopher Hussey

 TRACKS 17–18

Watch out for...

- The *anacruses* in this song — an *anacrusis* or *pickup* is a note (or group of notes) at the beginning of a phrase that precedes the downbeat of the first full measure of that phrase. You'll find examples of this at the very beginning into measure 1, on the last beat of measure 17 into 18, and on the last beat of measure 34 into 35.

  Can you spot some examples of an anacrusis in earlier songs?

Lightly and flowingly

The hol-ly and the i-vy, when they are both full-grown, of___

all the trees that are in the wood, the___ hol-ly bears the crown. O the

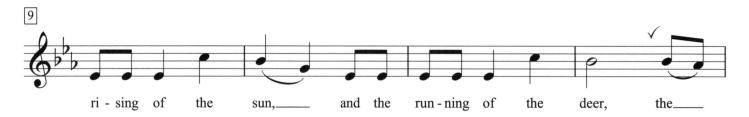

ri-sing of the sun,___ and the run-ning of the deer, the___

play-ing of the mer-ry or-gan, sweet sing-ing in the choir. The

hol - ly bears a blos - som as white as an - y flower; and___

Ma - ry bore sweet Je - sus Christ to___ be our sweet Sa - viour. O the *mf*

ri - sing of the sun,___ and the run - ning of the deer, the___

play - ing of the mer - ry or - gan, sweet sing - ing in the choir. *f* The

hol - ly bears a ber - ry as red as an - y blood; and___

Ma - ry bore sweet Je - sus Christ to___ do for sin - ners good. O the

ri - sing of the sun,___ and the run - ning of the deer, the___

play - ing of the mer - ry or - gan, sweet sing - ing in the choir.

We Three Kings Of Orient Are

Words & Music by John Henry Hopkins
Arranged by Christopher Hussey

TRACKS
19–20

Watch out for...

- The *repeat* sign at the end of measure 32 :|| — this tells you to repeat back from the very beginning.

- The key — this is the first song in this collection to be in a *minor* key: A minor. However, it doesn't stay in A minor for the whole song. From measure 17, while there is no new key signature, the music is in a *major* key.
Do you know which major key the second half of the song is in?

Smoothly

1st time: *mp*
2nd time: *mf*

We three kings of O - ri - ent are;

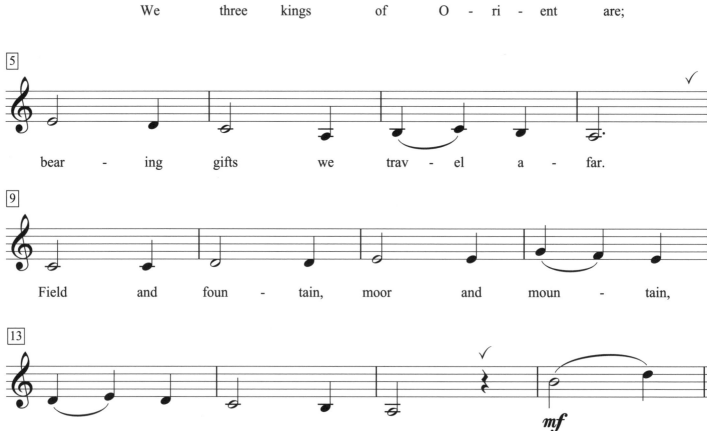

bear - ing gifts we trav - el a - far.

Field and foun - tain, moor and moun - tain,

fol - low - ing yon - der star. O_____
mf

star of won - der, star of night,

star with roy - al beau - ty bright;

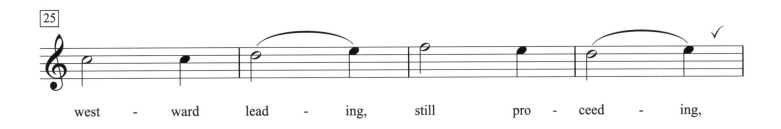

west - ward lead - ing, still pro - ceed - ing,

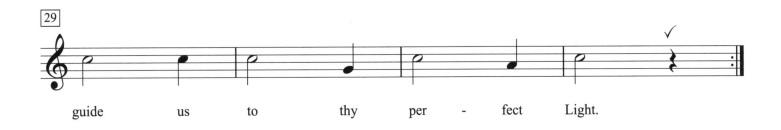

guide us to thy per - fect Light.

mp

God Rest Ye Merry, Gentlemen

Traditional English
Arranged by Christopher Hussey

**TRACKS
21–22**

♪ *Watch out for...*

- The articulation marks — *staccato* marks ♩ , *tenuto* marks ♩ and *accents* ♩ are used in this song, and there's also two passages marked *legato* (smoothly).

Making the difference between these types of articulation clear will give your performance more detail and character.

Steadily, with character

rest   ye   mer - ry,   gen - tle - men,   let   noth - ing   you   dis - may.   For

Je - sus   Christ   our   Sa - viour   was   born   on   Christ - mas   Day,   to

Rocking Carol

Words by Percy Dearmer
Music Traditional Czech
Arranged by Christopher Hussey

**TRACKS
23–24**

𝄞 **Watch out for...**

- The *accidentals* — some of the Gs in this melody have a ♯ before them, which isn't part of the key signature. The G naturals in the bars immediately following a G sharp have a 'cautionary' natural before them (♮), to remind you that they aren't to be played as sharps.

- The *hairpins* — this sign ⬱ indicates a **crescendo** for its duration, while ⬲ indicates a **diminuendo**. These will add expression to your performance.

Gently, with expression

Lit - tle Ba - by, sweet-ly___ sleep, do not___ stir; we will lend a___

coat of___ fur. We will rock You, rock You, rock___ You,

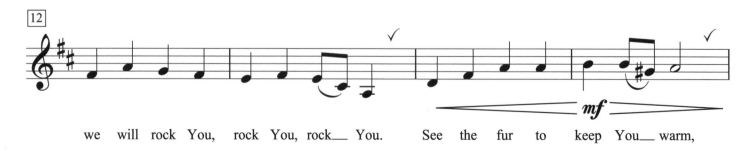

we will rock You, rock You, rock___ You. See the fur to keep You___ warm,

snug - ly____ round Your____ ti - ny____ form.

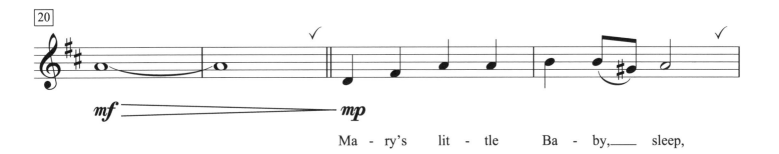

Ma - ry's lit - tle Ba - by,____ sleep,

sweet - ly____ sleep; sleep in____ com - fort____ slum - ber____ deep.

We will rock You, rock You, rock__ You, we will rock You, rock You, rock__ You.

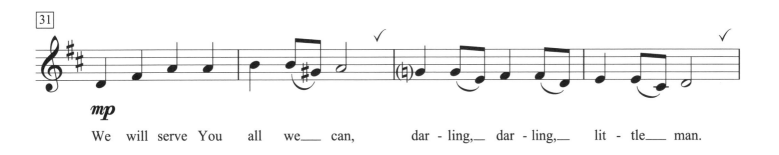

We will serve You all we__ can, dar - ling,__ dar - ling,__ lit - tle__ man.

O Christmas Tree (O Tannenbaum)

Traditional German
Arranged by Christopher Hussey

TRACKS
25–26

🎵 ***Watch out for...***

- The sixteenth notes ♪ — which last for a quarter of a beat and can be joined in groups like this: ♫ or ♫♫

In this song, they are used as part of a dotted eighth note-sixteenth note rhythm: Practise this rhythm on its own to begin with.

Enchantingly

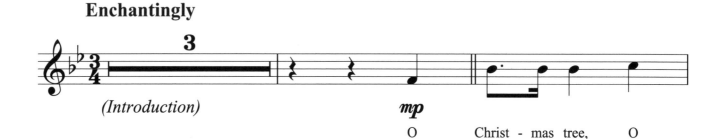

(Introduction)

mp

O Christ - mas tree, O

Christ-mas tree, thou tree most fair and love - ly! O Christ - mas tree, O

mf

Christ-mas tree, thou tree most fair and love - ly! The sight of thee at

mp

Christ - mas - tide spreads hope and glad - ness far and wide. O

I Saw Three Ships

Traditional English
Arranged by Christopher Hussey

**TRACKS
27–28**

𝄞 Watch out for...

- The time signature $\frac{6}{8}$ — this tells you there are six eighth notes in each measure.

  Unlike $\frac{3}{4}$ which also has six eighth notes in each measure, in $\frac{6}{8}$ the quavers are grouped in threes, so that there are two dotted quarter note beats in each measure. This is an example of a *compound meter*.

- The articulation in the last four measures.

With a lilt

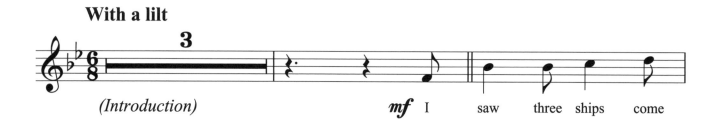

(Introduction) ... *mf* I saw three ships come

sail - ing in on Christ - mas Day, on Christ - mas Day, I

saw three ships come sail - ing in on Christ - mas Day in the

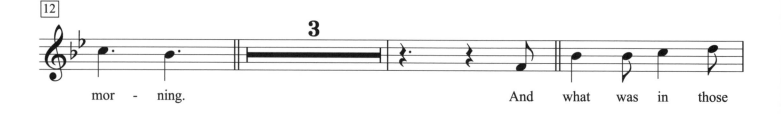

mor - ning. And what was in those

ships, all three, on Christ - mas Day, on Christ - mas Day? And

what was in those ships, all three, on Christ - mas Day in the

mor - ning? Our Sa - viour, Christ, and

His la - dy, on Christ - mas Day, on Christ - mas Day, our

Sa - viour, Christ, and His la - dy, on Christ - mas Day in the

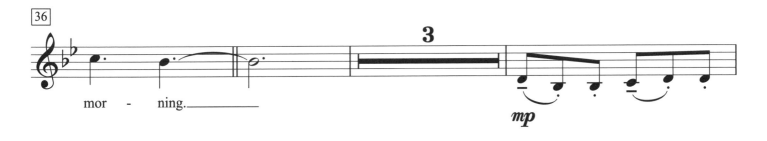

mor - ning.

The Twelve Days Of Christmas

Traditional, Arrangement & Additions by Frederic Austin
Arranged by Christopher Hussey

TRACKS 29–30

Watch out for...

- The changes of time signature between **4/4** and **3/4** — be sure to count carefully so that you play the music correctly.

- The *anacrusis* at the very beginning of the tune.

- The **D.S. al Coda** — when you reach this instruction, repeat the music from the sign 𝄋 until **To Coda** ⊕, then jump to the *coda*, marked ⊕ **CODA** , and play to the end.

- The number of verses is not the same as in the original song. Both this arrangement and the recordings jump to the last verse ('the twelfth day of Christmas') after the fifth day!

CD Track Listing

Exclusive Distributors:
Music Sales Limited
Newmarket Road, Bury St Edmunds, Suffolk IP33 3YB, UK.
Music Sales Pty Limited
Units 3-4, 17 Willfox Street, Condell Park NSW 2200, Australia.

Order No. WMR101398
ISBN: 978-1-78305-644-6

Edited by Sam Lung.
Exercises written by Christopher Hussey.
Music engraved by Camden Music Services.
Backing tracks composed and arranged by Christopher Hussey and Jeremy Birchall.
Trumpet by Richard Freeman.
CD recorded, mixed and mastered by Imogen Hall and Jonas Persson.

Printed in the EU.